MONET

First published in France by LAROUSSE in 2016
First published in Great Britain in 2017 by LOM Art, an imprint of
Michael O'Mara Books Limited
9 Lion Yard
Tremadoc Road
London SW4 7NQ

Publishing Director: Carine Girac-Marinier
Editorial Director: Christine Dauphant
Editor: Maëva Journo
Cover Design: Uli Meindl
Colouring Pages: Sandra Lebrun
Typesetting: Les PAOistes
Production: Donia Faiz

A CIP catalogue record for this book is available from the British Library.

Papers used by Michael O'Mara Books Limited are natural, recyclable
products made from wood grown in sustainable forests. The manufacturing
processes conform to the environmental regulations of the country of origin.

ISBN: 978-1-910552-68-1

2 3 4 5 6 7 8 9 10

Printed and bound in China

www.mombooks.com

MONET

COLOUR BY DOTS

LOM
ART

Claude Monet

irectly linked to the birth of Impressionism through his painting *Impression, Sunrise*, Claude Monet (1840-1926) became one of the leading figures of the movement that modernized nineteenth-century art. Nicknamed 'the Raphael of water' by Manet, he left behind a vast body of work.

Monet and his Masters

The second son of fabric merchant Adolphe Monet and singer Louise Justine, Claude Monet was raised in Le Havre. When his mother died in 1858, he left school, which had always 'felt like a prison' to him, and sold his first drawings. At this point he was to have a defining encounter with local painter Eugène Boudin, 'the king of the skies', as Charles Baudelaire called him. With Boudin, he began to work outdoors and grasp 'what painting can be'. He would go on to say of the Dutch painter Johan Barthold Jongkind, whom he met in 1862, 'It was he who completed the education of my eye.'

With his father's support, Monet arrived in Paris in 1859 to study painting. Rather than the École des Beaux-Arts, he enrolled at the Académie Suisse, where he became friendly with Camille Pissarro. In 1861, Monet was sent to Algeria as a member of the First Regiment of African Light Cavalry. The light and colour he witnessed during his military service would go on to influence his later artistic studies.

Between Paris and Normandy

In 1862, Monet joined the studio of Swiss painter Charles Gleyre, working alongside Alfred Sisley, Auguste Renoir and Frédéric Bazille, who would become a great friend. Through Bazille, he discovered the village of Chailly, close to Barbizon, and returned to Normandy. At the 1865 Salon, he exhibited two critically acclaimed seascapes. From the 1860s onwards, the painter divided his time between the Paris area and Normandy and developed a style similar to that of Édouard Manet, using a palette of radiant, warm colours. At this stage, light was used in patches but was not yet the main focus of his pictures. But as Monet's style became more defined, the Salons began closing their doors to him, and in 1870, none of his paintings were accepted.

The Primacy of Vision

In 1872, Claude Monet settled in Argenteuil, joining Manet and Renoir, among others – the Impressionist group was coming together. Having set up a boat studio, Monet aimed to capture snapshots of the changing light on the banks of the Seine and the surrounding countryside; besides the seminal canvas *Impression, Sunrise*, most likely painted at Le Havre, he produced *Regattas at Argenteuil*, *Poppy Field* and *The Port at Argenteuil*.

'There must be some impression in it.'

In 1874, the photographer Nadar provided his Paris studio as the venue for the first exhibition of the group of independent painters to which Monet belonged, whose members had been routinely excluded from the official Salons. Of the 165 canvases displayed, eight were by Claude Monet – *Impression, Sunrise* among them. Louis Leroy, a critic from satirical newspaper *Le Charivari*, described his reaction to the painting: 'What does this picture show? Check the catalogue. *Impression, Sunrise*. Impression – I was certain of it. I was just telling myself that, since I was impressed, there must be some impression in it.' And so it was that the year 1874 marked the height of Impressionism as a movement, in spite of the critical jibes.

After several of his paintings were acquired by Manet, Monet was able to move to Vétheuil, on a bend in the River Seine, in 1878. Parisian scenes gave way to views of the village. Hungry for recognition and success, Monet once again put himself forward for the official Salon in 1880 and had one painting accepted, but very poorly displayed. This was also the year of his first solo exhibition, organized by magazine *La Vie Moderne*. Thanks to regular custom from art dealer Durand-Ruel, Monet could now do without the Salons and meet the cost of moving first to Poissy in 1881 and then to Giverny in 1883.

Giverny, Haven of Peace and Light

Giverny was to become the haven of peace and happiness Monet had always dreamed of, as his many paintings of it show. During the 1880s, he travelled a great deal, to the South of France (1883-4 and again in 1888), the Netherlands (1886), Belle-Île, off the coast of Brittany, (1886) and the Creuse valley (1889).

But wherever he went, Monet's thoughts always returned to Giverny, where he was finally able to buy his house in 1890. Though he continued to travel to Norway, London and Italy, his garden remained his ultimate source of inspiration: with his 'Water Lilies' series and its alchemical mixture of plants, reflections and patterns of light, Impressionism came close to abstraction.

From this point on, the artist's work began to sell for unprecedented sums and he made his debut at the Louvre. But he also witnessed the passing of many of those dear to him: Pissarro, Renoir, his wife Alice, and his son Jean, whose widow was at his side when Monet died of exhaustion in 1926.

Getting started

Some colours have been slightly adapted in order to make the design easier to follow and the finished result better defined.

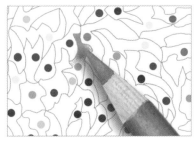

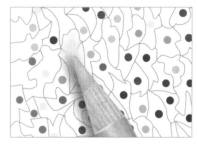

1 Start by gathering all the colours used on the colouring page. Colouring pencils, felt-tip pens and paints all work well.

2 Colour each section to match the dot within it.

3 For a uniform effect when colouring large areas, work in several directions, using circular motions.

4 To blend the different sections together and blur the lines between them, overlap colours at the edges.

5 If you don't have the right shade for a section, try layering multiple colours to achieve the desired effect. You can also replace a missing colour with another similar shade for a more personalized result.

Colouring Pages

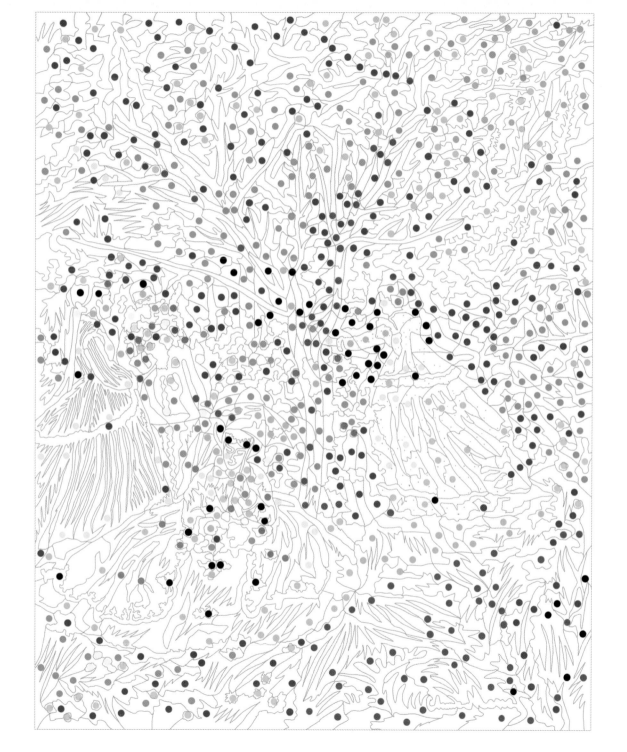

$N°2$

Original painting page 57

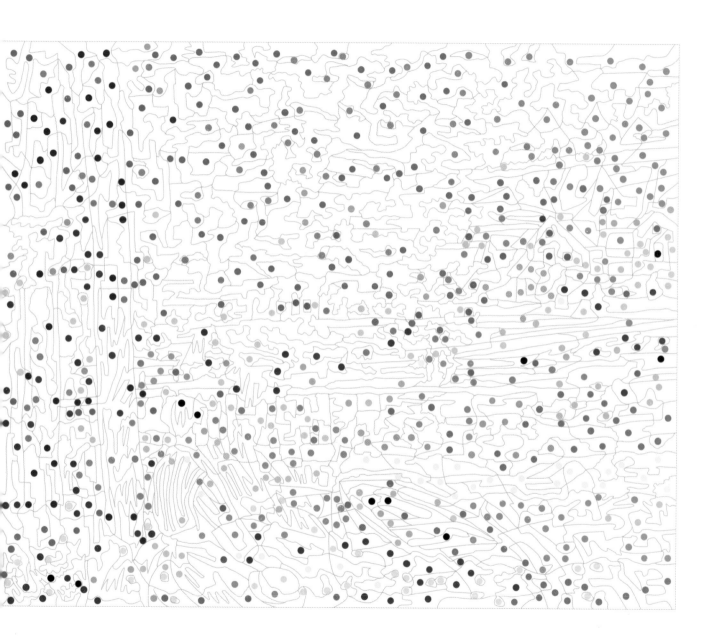

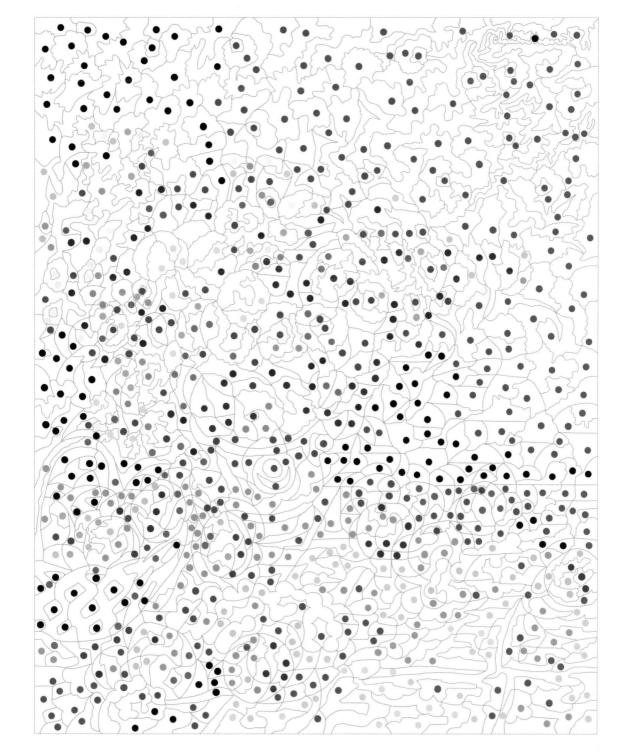

15

N°4

Original painting page 61

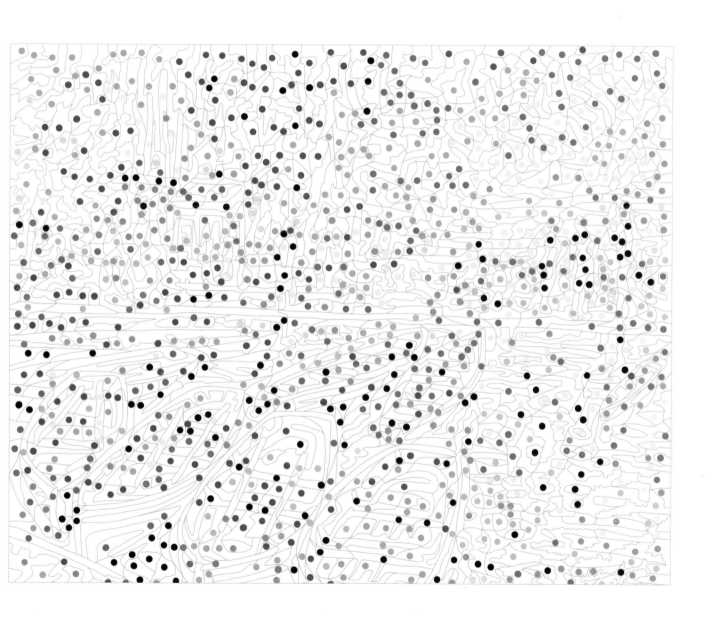

$N^\circ5$

Original painting page 63

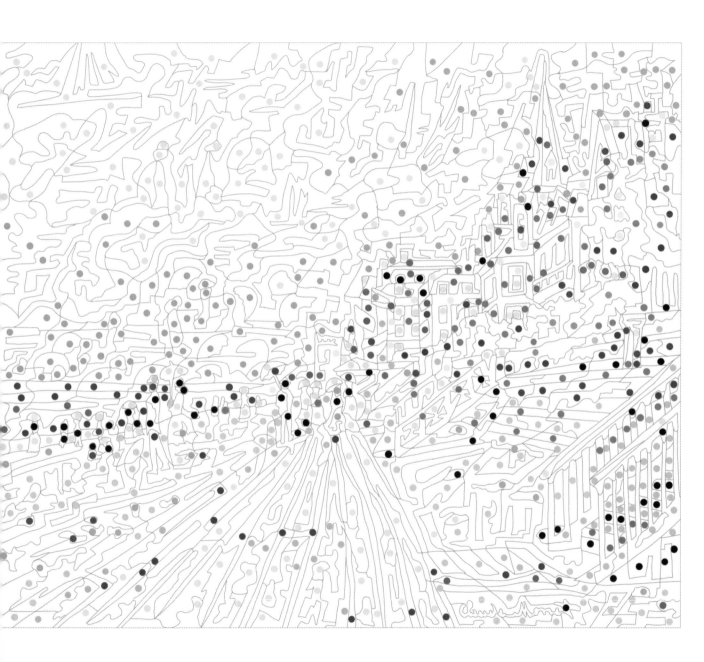

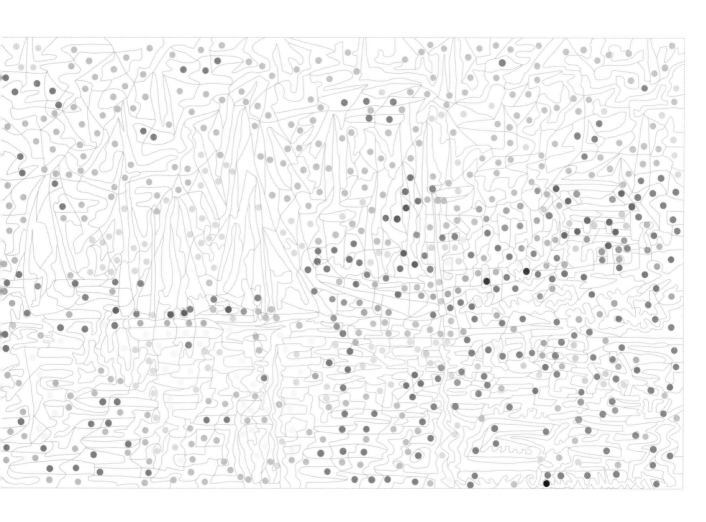

N°7
Original painting page 67

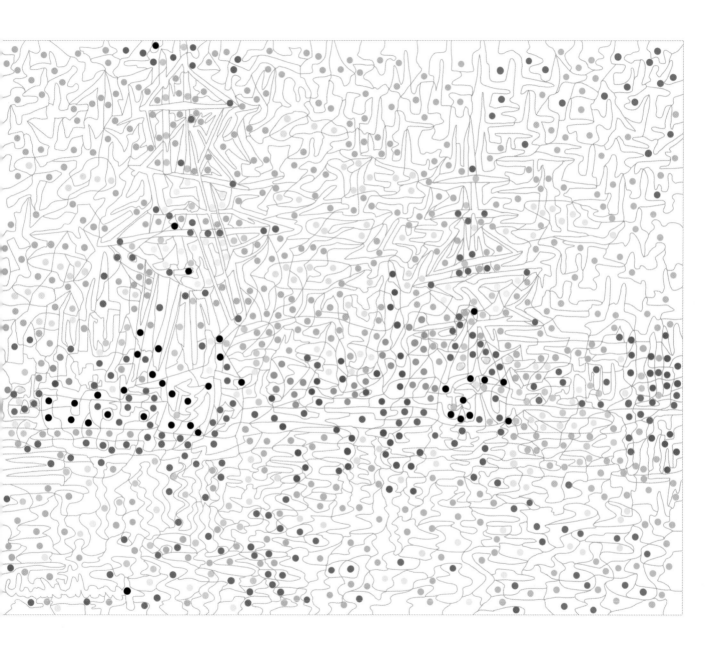

$N°8$

Original painting page 69

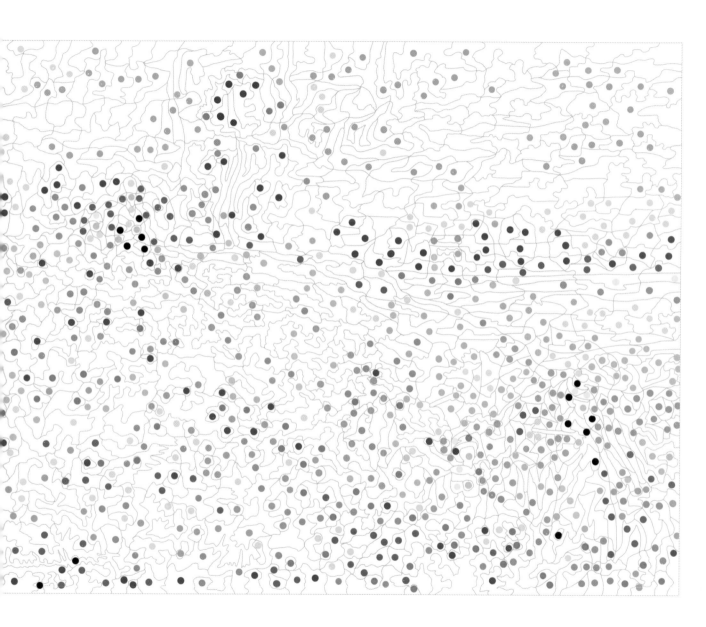

N°9

Original painting page 71

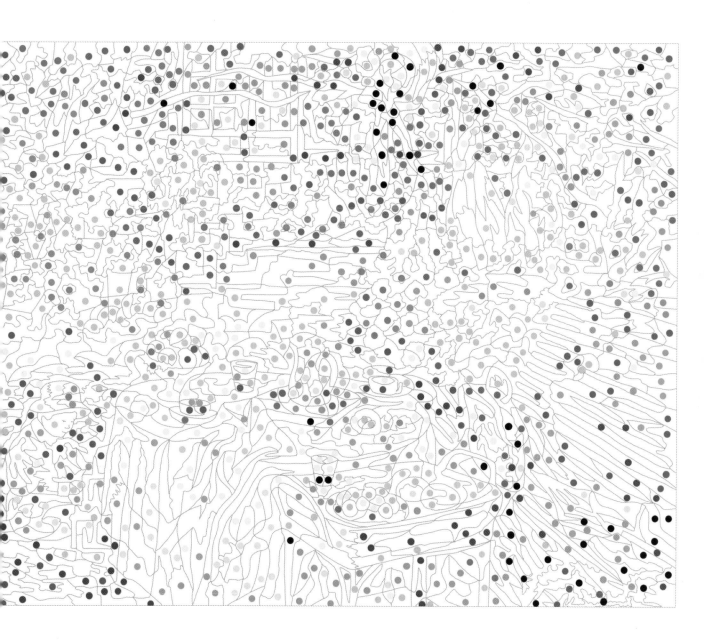

N°10
Original painting page 73

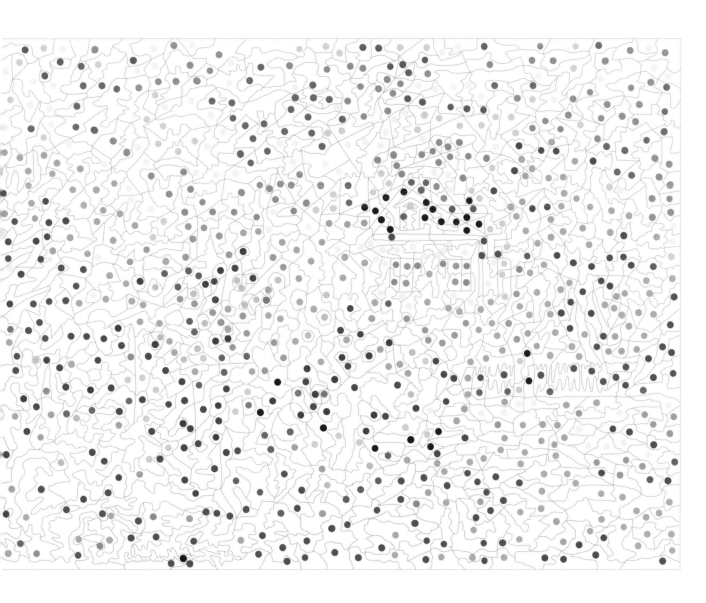

$\mathcal{N}°11$

Original painting page 75

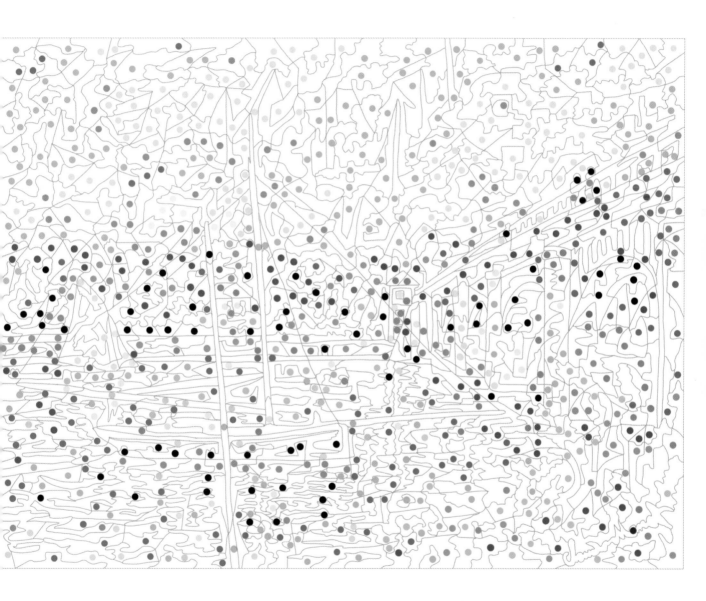

N°12

Original painting page 77

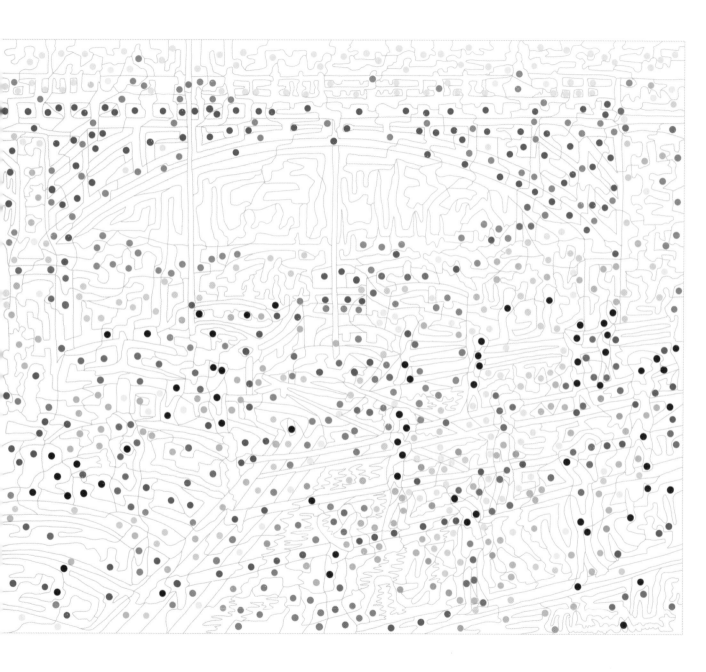

N°13
Original painting page 79

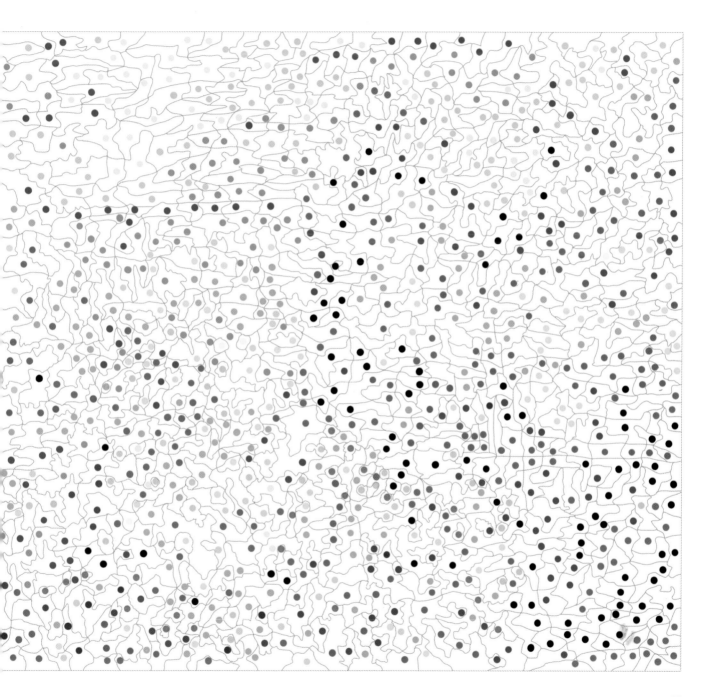

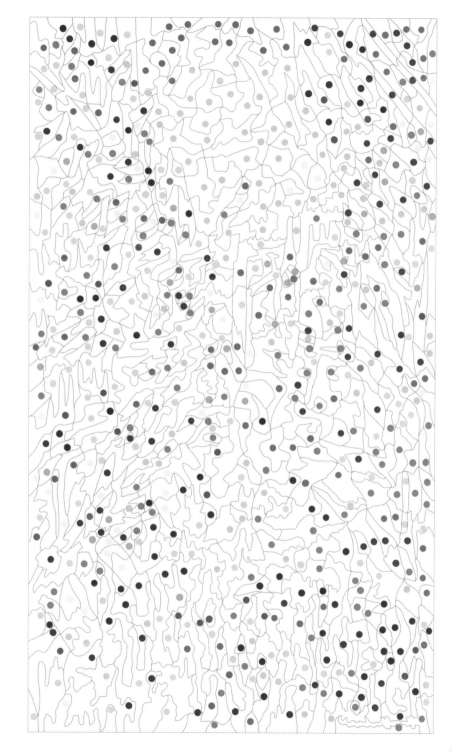

39

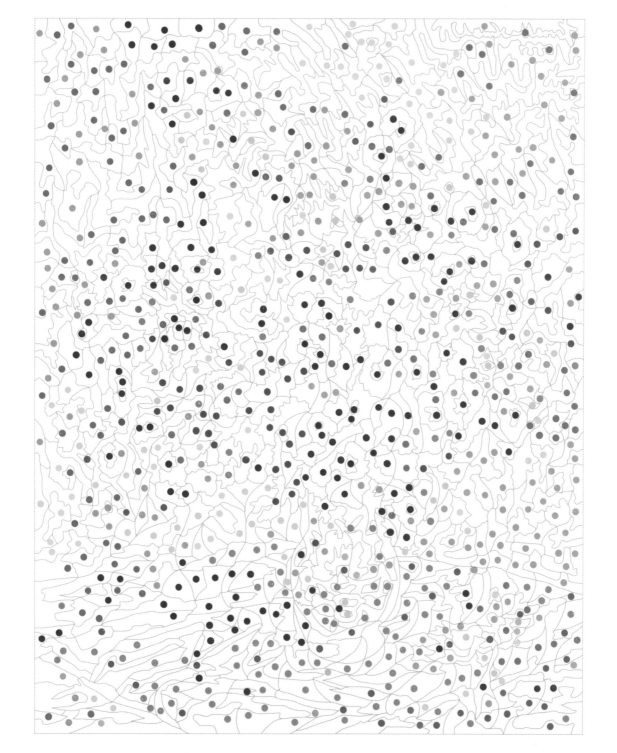

N°17
Original painting page 87

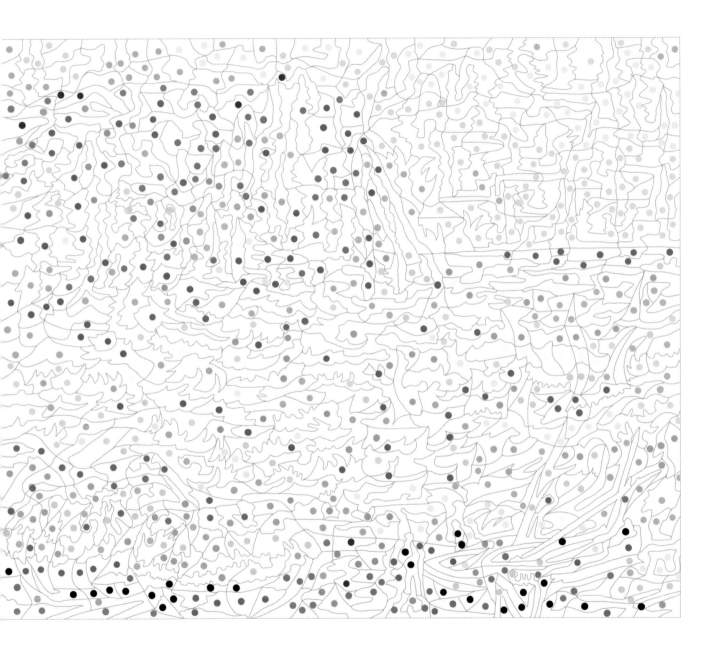

43

N°18

Original painting page 89

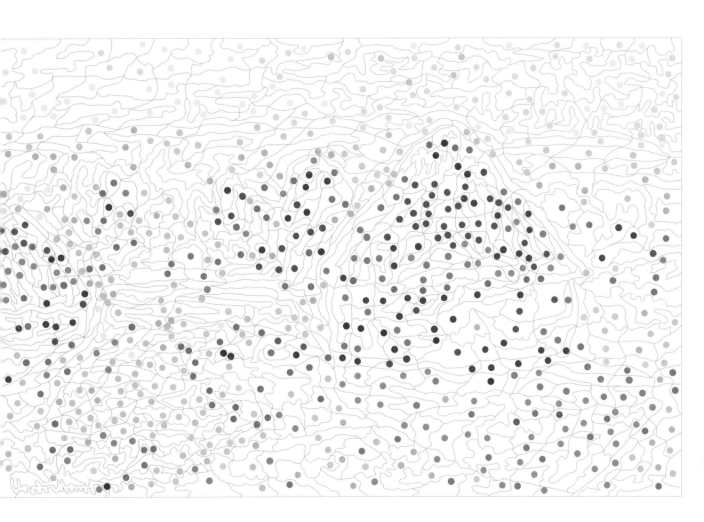

45

N°19

Original painting page 91

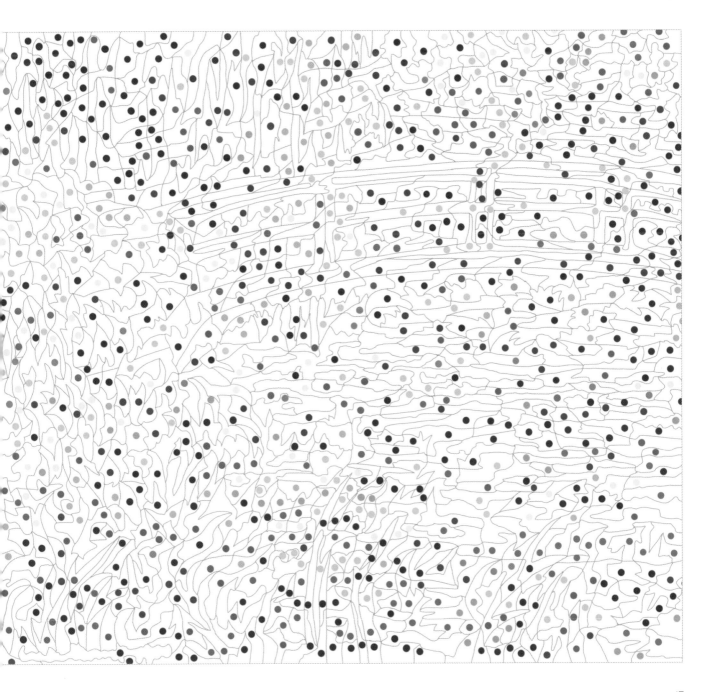

47

N°20

Original painting page 93

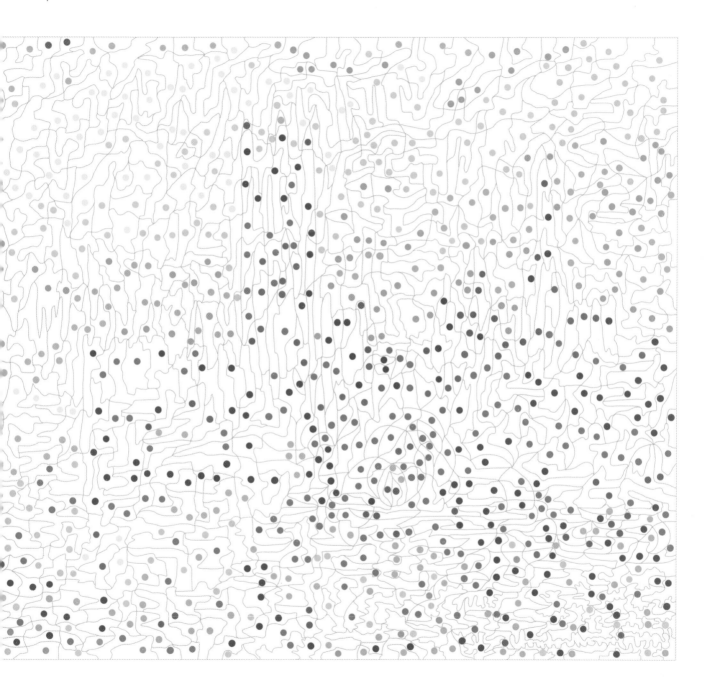

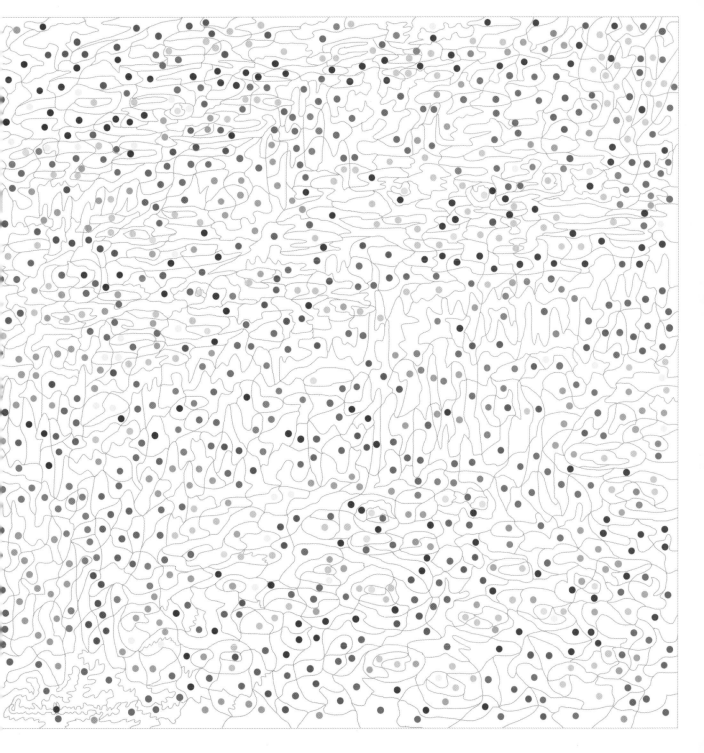

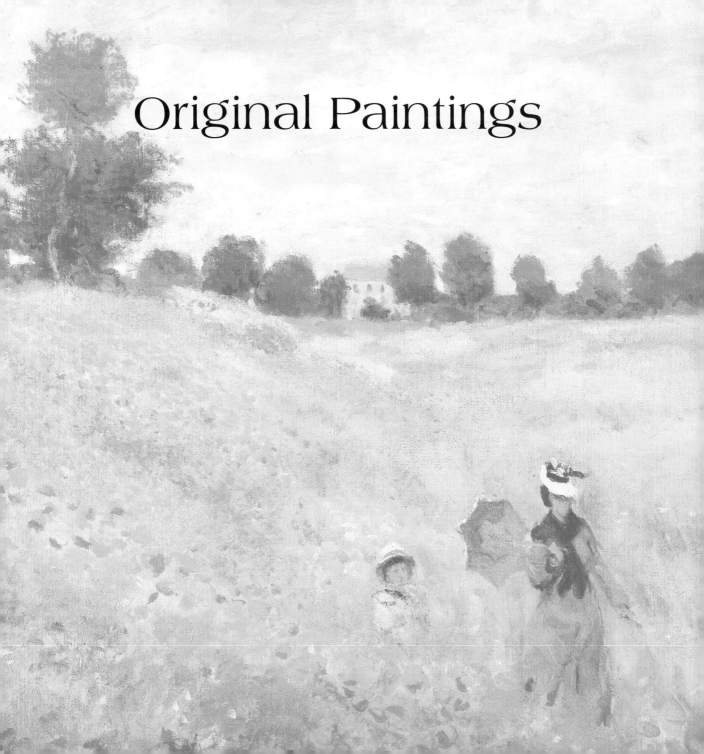

Original Paintings

N°1

page 11

Women in the Garden (1866)

N° 2

page 13

On the Bank of the Seine, Bennecourt (1868)

N° 3

page 15

Still Life with Flowers and Fruit (1869)

N° 4

page 17

Bathers at La Grenouillère (1869)

N°5
page 19
The Beach at Trouville (1870)

Claude Monet

N°6
page 21
Regattas at Argenteuil (1872)

N°7

page 23

Ships Riding on the Seine at Rouen (1872-3)

$N°8$

page 25

Poppy Field (1873)

N°9

page 27
The Luncheon (1873)

N°10
page 29
The Artist's Garden in Argenteuil (1873)

N°11
page 31
The Bridge at Argenteuil (1874)

N°12
page 33
The Coalmen (1875)

N°13

page 35

Corner of the Garden at Montgeron (or The Dahlias) (1876)

N°14
page 37
Turkeys (1877)

N°15

page 39

The Rue Montorgueil (1878)

N°16
page 41
Red Chrysanthemums (1880)

N°17
page 43
Stormy Seas at Étretat (1883)

N°18

page 45

Haystacks (Midday) (1890)

89

N°19
page 47
Water Lily Pond, Symphony in Rose (1900)

N°20
page 49
The Houses of Parliament (1903)

N°21
page 51
Water Lilies (1916)

PHOTOGRAPHIC CREDITS